JAMES HERRIOT

SEVEN YORKSHIRE TALES

PENGUIN BOOKS

PENGUIN BOOKS

Published by the Penguin Group. Penguin Books Ltd, 27 Wrights Lane, London W8 5TZ, England. Penguin Books USA Inc., 375 Hudson Street, New York, New York 10014, USA. Penguin Books Australia Ltd, Ringwood, Victoria, Australia. Penguin Books Canada, 10 Alcorn Avenue, Toronto, Ontario, Canada M4V 3B2. Penguin Books (NZ) Ltd, 182–190 Wairau Road, Auckland 10, New Zealand · Penguin Books Ltd, Registered Offices: Harmondsworth, Middlesex, England · **These stories have been taken from *It Shouldn't Happen to a Vet*, *Let Sleeping Vets Lie*, *Vets Might Fly* and *Every Living Thing* by James Herriot, published by Penguin Books in 1972, 1973, 1976, 1992 respectively**. This edition published 1995 · Typeset by Datix International Limited, Bungay, Suffolk · Printed in England by Clays Ltd, St Ives plc · 10 9 8 7 6 5 4 3 2

CONTENTS

The Girl in Green Trousers

Many of the Dales farms were anonymous and it was a help to find this one so plainly identified. 'HESTON GRANGE' it said on the gate in bold black capitals.

I got out of the car and undid the latch. It was a good gate, too, and swung easily on its hinges instead of having to be dragged round with a shoulder under the top spar. The farmhouse lay below me, massive, grey-stoned, with a pair of bow windows which some prosperous Victorian had added to the original structure.

It stood on a flat, green neck of land in a loop of the river and the lushness of the grass and the quiet fertility of the surrounding fields contrasted sharply with the stark hills behind. Towering oaks and beeches sheltered the house and a thick pine wood covered the lower slopes of the fell.

I walked round the buildings shouting as I always did, because some people considered it a subtle insult to go to the house and ask if the farmer was in. Good farmers are indoors only at meal times. But my shouts drew no reply, so I went over and knocked at the door set deep among the weathered stones.

A voice answered, 'Come in,' and I opened the door into a huge, stone-flagged kitchen with hams and sides of bacon hanging from hooks in the ceiling. A dark-haired girl in a check blouse and green linen trousers was kneading dough in a bowl. She looked up and smiled.

'Sorry I couldn't let you in. I've got my hands full.' She held up her arms, floury-white to the elbow.

'That's all right. My name is Herriot. I've come to see a calf. It's lame, I understand.'

'Yes, we think he's broken his leg. Probably got his foot in a hole when he was running about. If you don't mind waiting a minute, I'll come with you. My father and the men are in the fields. I'm Helen Alderson, by the way.'

She washed and dried her arms and pulled on a pair of short wellingtons. 'Take over this bread, will you, Meg?' she said to an old woman who came through from an inner room. 'I have to show Mr Herriot the calf.'

Outside, she turned to me and laughed. 'We've got a bit of a walk, I'm afraid. He's in one of the top buildings. Look, you can just see it up there.' She pointed to a squat, stone barn, high on the fellside. I knew all about these top buildings; they were scattered all over the high country, and I got a lot of healthy exercise going round them. They were used for storing hay and other things and as shelters for the animals on the hill pastures.

I looked at the girl for a few seconds. 'Oh, that's all right, I don't mind. I don't mind in the least.'

We went over the field to a narrow bridge spanning the river, and, following her across, I was struck by a thought; this new fashion of women wearing trousers might be a bit revolutionary, but there was a lot to be said for it. The path led upward through the pine wood, and here the sunshine was broken up into islands of brightness among the dark trunks, the sound of the river grew faint and we walked softly on a thick carpet of pine needles. It was cool in the wood and silent except when a bird call echoed through the trees.

Ten minutes of hard walking brought us out again into the hot sun on the open moor and the path curved steeper still round a series of rocky outcrops. I was beginning to puff, but the girl kept up a brisk pace, swinging along with easy strides. I was glad when we reached the level ground on the top and the barn came in sight again.

When I opened the half-door I could hardly see my patient in the dark interior, which was heavy with the fragrance of hay piled nearly to the roof. He looked very small and sorry for himself, with his dangling foreleg which trailed uselessly along the strawed floor as he tried to walk.

'Will you hold his head while I examine him, please?' I said.

The girl caught the calf expertly, one hand under its chin, the other holding an ear. As I felt my way over the leg the little creature stood trembling, his face a picture of woe.

'Well, your diagnosis was correct. Clean fracture of the radius and ulna, but there's very little displacement, so it should do well with a plaster on it.' I opened my bag, took out some plaster bandages then filled a bucket with water from a nearby spring. I soaked one of the bandages and applied it to the leg, following it with a second and a third until the limb was encased in a rapidly hardening white sheath from elbow to foot.

'We'll just wait a couple of minutes till it hardens, then we can let him go.' I kept tapping the plaster until I was satisfied it was set like stone. 'All right,' I said finally. 'He can go now.'

The girl released the head and the little animal trotted away. 'Look,' she cried. 'He's putting his weight on it already! And doesn't he look a lot happier!' I smiled. I felt I had really done something. The calf felt no pain now that the broken ends of the bone were immobilized; and the fear which always demoralizes a hurt animal had magically vanished.

'Yes,' I said. 'He certainly has perked up quickly.' My words were almost drowned by a tremendous bellow and the patch of blue above the half-door was suddenly obscured by a large, shaggy head. Two great liquid eyes stared down anxiously at the little calf, and it answered with a high-pitched bawl. Soon a deafening duet was in progress.

'That's his mother,' the girl shouted above the din. 'Poor old thing, she's been hanging about here all morning wondering what we've done with her calf. She hates being separated from him.'

I straightened up and drew the bolt on the door. 'Well, she can come in now.'

The big cow almost knocked me down as she rushed past. Then she started a careful, sniffing inspection of her calf, pushing him around with her muzzle and making muffled lowing noises deep in her throat.

The little creature submitted happily to all the fuss, and when it was over and his mother was finally satisfied, he limped round to her udder and began to suck heartily.

'Soon got his appetite back,' I said and we both laughed.

I threw the empty plaster containers into my bag and closed it. 'He'll have to keep the plaster on for a month, so if you'll give me a ring then, I'll come back and take it off. Just keep an eye on him and make sure his leg doesn't get sore around the top of the bandage.'

As we left the barn the sunshine and the sweet warm air met us like a high wave. I turned and looked across the valley to the soaring green heights, smooth, enormous, hazy in the noon heat. Beneath my feet the grassy slopes fell away steeply to where the river glimmered among the trees.

'It's wonderful up here,' I said. 'Just look at that gorge over there. And that great hill – I suppose you could call it a mountain.' I pointed at a giant which heaved its heather-mottled shoulders high above the others.

'That's Heskit Fell – nearly two and a half thousand feet. And that's Eddleton just beyond, and Wedder Fell on the other side and Colver and Sennor.' The names with their wild, Nordic ring fell easily from her tongue; she spoke of them like old friends, and I could sense the affection in her voice.

We sat down on the warm grass of the hillside. A soft breeze pulled at the heads of the moorland flowers, and somewhere a curlew cried. Darrowby and Skeldale House and veterinary practice seemed a thousand miles away.

'You're lucky to live here,' I said. 'But I don't think you need me to tell you that.'

'No, I love this place. There's nowhere else quite like it.' She paused and looked slowly around her. 'I'm glad it appeals to you too – a lot of people find it too bare and wild. It almost seems to frighten them.'

I laughed. 'Yes, I know, but as far as I'm concerned I can't help feeling sorry for all the thousands of vets who don't work in the Yorkshire Dales.'

I began to talk about my work, then almost without knowing, I was going back over my student days, telling her of the good times, the friends I had made and our hopes and aspirations.

I surprised myself with my flow of talk – I wasn't much of a chatterbox usually – and I felt I must be boring my companion. But she sat quietly looking over the valley, her arms around her green-clad legs, nodding at times as though she understood. And she laughed in all the right places.

I wondered, too, at the silly feeling that I would like to forget all about the rest of the day's duty and stay up here on this sunny hillside. It came to me that it had been a long time since I had sat down and talked to a girl of my own age. I had almost forgotten what it was like.

I didn't hurry back down the path and through the scented pine wood but it seemed no time at all before we were walking across the wooden bridge and over the field to the farm.

I turned with my hand on the car door. 'Well, I'll see you in a month.' It sounded like an awful long time.

The girl smiled. 'Thank you for what you've done.' As I started the engine she waved and went into the house.

'Helen Alderson?' my partner, Siegfried, said later over lunch. 'Of course, I know her. Lovely girl.'

Siegfried's brother, Tristan, across the table, made no comment, but he laid down his knife and fork, raised his eyes reverently to the ceiling and gave a long, low whistle. Then he started to eat again.

Siegfried went on. 'Oh, yes, I know her very well. And I admire her. Her mother died a few years ago and she runs the whole place. Cooks and looks after her father and a younger brother and sister.' He spooned some mashed potatoes on to his plate. 'Any men friends? Oh, half the young bloods in the district are chasing her but she doesn't seem to be going steady with any of them. Choosy sort, I think.'

The Farmer's Hospitality

'Monday morning disease' they used to call it, the almost unbelievably gross thickening of the hind limb of cart horses which had stood in the stable over the weekend. It seemed that the sudden suspension of their normal work and exercise produced the massive swelling which gave many a farmer a nasty jolt right at the beginning of the week.

But it was Wednesday evening now, and Mr Crump's big Shire gelding was greatly improved.

'That leg's less than half the size it was,' I said, running my hand over the inside of the hock, feeling the remains of the lump pitting under my fingers. 'I can see you've put in some hard work here.'

'Aye, ah did as you said.' Mr Crump's reply was typically laconic, but I knew he must have spent hours fomenting and massaging the limb and forcibly exercising the horse as I had told him when I gave the injection on Monday.

I began to fill the syringe for a repeat injection. 'He's having no corn, is he?'

'Nay, nowt but bran.'

'That's fine. I think he'll be back to normal in a day or two if you keep up the treatment.'

The farmer grunted and no sign of approval showed in the big, purple-red face with its perpetually surprised expression.

But I knew he was pleased all right; he was fond of the horse and had been unable to hide his concern at the animal's pain and distress on my first visit.

I went into the house to wash my hands and Mr Crump led the way into the kitchen, his big frame lumbering clumsily ahead of me. He proffered soap and towel in his slow-moving way and stood back in silence as I leaned over the long shallow sink of brown earthenware.

As I dried my hands he cleared his throat and spoke hesitantly. 'Would you like a drink of ma wine?'

Before I could answer, Mrs Crump came bustling through from an inner room. She was pulling on her hat and behind her her teenage son and daughter followed, dressed ready to go out.

'Oh, Albert, stop it!' she snapped, looking up at her husband. 'Mr Herriot doesn't want your wine. I wish you wouldn't pester people so with it!'

The boy grinned. 'Dad and his wine, he's always looking for a victim.' His sister joined in the general laughter and I had an uncomfortable feeling that Mr Crump was the odd man out in his own home.

'We're going down t'village institute to see the school play, Mr Herriot,' the wife said briskly. 'We're late now, so we must be off.' She hurried away with her children, leaving the big man looking after her sheepishly.

There was a silence while I finished drying my hands, then I turned to the farmer. 'Well, how about that drink, Mr Crump?'

He hesitated for a moment and the surprised look deepened. 'Would you . . . you'd really like to try some?'

'I'd love to. I haven't had my evening meal yet – I could just do with an aperitif.'

'Right, I'll be back in a minute.' He disappeared into the large pantry at the end of the kitchen and came back with a bottle of amber liquid and glasses.

'This is ma rhubarb,' he said, tipping out two good measures.

I took a sip and then a good swallow, and gasped as the liquid blazed a fiery trail down to my stomach.

'It's strong stuff,' I said a little breathlessly, 'but the taste is very pleasant. Very pleasant indeed.'

Mr Crump watched approvingly as I took another drink. 'Aye, it's just right. Nearly two years old.'

I drained the glass and this time the wine didn't burn so much on its way down but seemed to wash around the walls of my empty stomach and send glowing tendrils creeping along my limbs.

'Delicious,' I said. 'Absolutely delicious.'

The farmer expanded visibly. He refilled the glasses and watched with rapt attention as I drank. When we had finished the second glass he jumped to his feet.

'Now for a change I want you to try summat different.' He almost trotted to the pantry and produced another bottle, this time of colourless fluid. 'Elderflower,' he said, panting slightly.

When I tasted it I was amazed at the delicate flavour, the bubbles sparkling and dancing on my tongue.

'Gosh, this is terrific! It's just like champagne. You know, you really have a gift – I never thought home-made wines could taste like this.'

Mr Crump stared at me for a moment, then one corner of his mouth began to twitch and, incredibly, a shy smile spread slowly over his face. 'You're about fust I've heard say that. You'd think I was trying to poison folks when I offer them ma wine – they always shy off but they can sup plenty of beer and whisky.'

'Well, they don't know what they're missing, Mr Crump.' I watched while the farmer replenished my glass. 'I wouldn't have believed you could make stuff as good as this at home.' I sipped appreciatively at the elderflower. It still tasted like champagne.

I hadn't got more than halfway down the glass before Mr Crump was clattering and clinking inside the pantry again. He emerged with a bottle with contents of a deep blood-red. 'Try that,' he gasped.

I was beginning to feel like a professional taster and rolled the first mouthful around my mouth with eyes half closed. 'Mm, mm, yes. Just like an excellent port, but there's something else here – a fruitiness in the background – something familiar about it – it's . . . it's . . .'

'Blackberry!' shouted Mr Crump triumphantly. 'One of t'best I've done. Made it two back-ends since – it were a right good year for it.'

Leaning back in the chair, I took another drink of the rich, dark wine; it was round-flavoured, warming, and behind it there was always the elusive hint of brambles. I could almost see the heavy-hanging clusters of berries glistening black and succulent in the autumn sunshine. The mellowness of the image matched my mood, which was becoming more expansive by the minute, and I looked around with leisurely appreciation at the rough comfort of the farmhouse kitchen; at the hams and sides of bacon hanging from their hooks in the ceiling, and at my host sitting across the table, watching me eagerly. He was, I noticed for the first time, still wearing his cap.

'You know,' I said, holding the glass high and studying its ruby depths against the light, 'I can't make up my mind which of your wines I like best. They're all excellent and yet so different.'

Mr Crump, too, had relaxed. He threw back his head and laughed delightedly before hurriedly refilling both of our tumblers. 'But you haven't started yet. Ah've got dozens of bottles in there – all different. You must try a few more.' He shambled again over to the pantry and this time when he reappeared he was weighed down by an armful of bottles of differing shapes and colours.

What a charming man he was, I thought. How wrong I had been in my previous assessment of him; it had been so easy to put him down as lumpish and unemotional, but as I looked at him now his face was alight with friendship, hospitality, understanding. He had cast off his inhibitions, and as he sat down surrounded by the latest batch he began to talk rapidly and fluently about wines and wine making.

Wide-eyed and impassioned he ranged at length over the niceties of fermentation and sedimentation, of flavour and bouquet. He dealt learnedly with the relative merits of Chambertin and Nuits St George, Montrachet and Chablis. Enthusiasts are appealing, but a fanatic is irresistible, and I sat spellbound while Mr Crump pushed endless samples of his craft in front of me, mixing and adjusting expertly.

'How did you find that 'un?'

'Very nice . . .'

'Bit sweet, maybe?'

'Well, perhaps . . .'

'Right, try some of this with it.' The meticulous addition of a few drops of nameless liquid from the packed rows of bottles. 'How's that?'

'Marvellous!'

'Now this 'un. Perhaps a bit sharpish, eh?'

'Possibly . . . yes . . .'

Again the tender trickling of a few mysterious droplets into my drink and again the anxious inquiry.

'Is that better?'

'Just right.'

The big man drank with me, glass by glass. We tried parsnip and dandelion, cowslip and parsley, clover, gooseberry, beetroot and crab apple. Incredibly we had some stuff made from turnips which was so exquisite that I insisted on a refill.

Everything gradually slowed down as we sat there. Time slowed down until it was finally meaningless. Mr Crump and

I slowed down and our speech and actions became more and more deliberate. The farmer's visits to the pantry developed into laboured, unsteady affairs; sometimes he took a roundabout route to reach the door and on one occasion there was a tremendous crash from within and I feared he had fallen among his bottles. But I couldn't be bothered to get up to see, and in due course he reappeared, apparently unharmed.

It was around nine o'clock that I heard the soft knocking on the outer door. I ignored it as I didn't want to interrupt Mr Crump, who was in the middle of a deep exposition.

'Thish,' he was saying, leaning close to me and tapping a bulbous flagon with his forefinger, 'thish is, my 'pinion, comp'rable to a fine Moselle. Made it lash year and would 'preciate it if you'd tell me what you think.' He bent low over the glass, blinking, heavy-eyed as he poured.

'Now then, wha' d'you say? Ish it or ishn't it?'

I took a gulp and paused for a moment. It all tasted the same now and I had never drunk Moselle anyway, but I nodded and hiccuped solemnly in reply.

The farmer rested a friendly hand on my shoulder and was about to make a further speech when he, too, heard the knocking. He made his way across the floor with some difficulty and opened the door. A young lad was standing there and I heard a few muttered words.

'We 'ave a cow on calving and we 'phoned surgery and they said vitnery might still be here.'

Mr Crump turned to face me. 'It's the Bamfords of Holly Bush. They wan' you to go there – jush a mile along t'road.'

'Right,' I heaved myself to my feet then gripped the table tightly as the familiar objects of the room began to whirl rapidly around me. When they came to rest Mr Crump appeared to be standing at the head of a fairly steep slope. The kitchen floor had seemed perfectly level when I had come in, but now it was all I could do to fight my way up the gradient.

When I reached the door Mr Crump was staring owlishly into the darkness.

''Sraining,' he said. ''sraining like 'ell.'

I peered out at the steady beat of the dark water on the cobbles of the yard, but my car was just a few yards away and I was about to set out when the farmer caught my arm.

'Jus' minute, can't go out like that.' He held up a finger then went over and groped about in a drawer. At length he produced a tweed cap which he offered me with great dignity.

I never wore anything on my head whatever the weather but I was deeply touched and wrung my companion's hand in silence. It was understandable that a man like Mr Crump, who wore his cap at all times, indoors and out, would recoil in horror from the idea of anybody venturing uncovered into the rain.

The tweed cap which I now put on was the biggest I had ever seen; a great round flat pancake of a thing which even at that moment I felt would keep not only my head but my shoulders and entire body dry in the heaviest downpour.

I took my leave of Mr Crump with reluctance, and as I

settled in the seat of the car trying to remember where first gear was situated I could see his bulky form silhouetted against the light from the kitchen; he was waving his hand with gentle benevolence and it struck me as I at length drove away what a deep and wonderful friendship had been forged that night.

Driving at walking pace along the dark narrow road, my nose almost touching the windscreen, I was conscious of some unusual sensations. My mouth and lips felt abnormally sticky as though I had been drinking liquid glue instead of wine, my breath seemed to be whistling in my nostrils like a strong wind blowing under a door, and I was having difficulty focusing my eyes. Fortunately I met only one car and as it approached and flashed past in the other direction I was muzzily surprised by the fact that it had two complete sets of headlights which kept merging into each other and drawing apart again.

In the yard at Holly Bush I got out of the car, nodded to the shadowy group of figures standing there, fumbled my bottle of antiseptic and calving ropes from the boot and marched determinedly into the byre. One of the men held an oil lamp over a cow lying on a deep bed of straw in one of the standings; from the vulva a calf's foot protruded a few inches and as the cow strained a little muzzle showed momentarily then disappeared as she relaxed.

Far away inside me a stone-cold-sober veterinary surgeon murmured: 'Only a leg back and a big roomy cow. Shouldn't be much trouble.' I turned and looked at the Bamfords for the first time. I hadn't met them before but it was easy to classify them; simple, kindly, anxious-to-please people – two middle-aged men, probably brothers, and two young men, who would be the sons of one or the other. They were all staring at me in the dim light, their eyes expectant, their mouths slightly open as though ready to smile or laugh if given half a chance.

I squared my shoulders, took a deep breath and said in a loud voice: 'Would you please bring me a bucket of hot water, some soap and a towel.' Or at least that's what I meant to say, because what actually issued from my lips was a torrent of something that sounded like Swahili. The Bamfords, poised, ready to spring into action to do my bidding, looked at me blankly. I cleared my throat, swallowed, took a few seconds' rest and tried again. The result was the same – another volley of gibberish echoing uselessly round the cow house.

Clearly I had a problem. It was essential to communicate in some way, particularly since these people didn't know me and were waiting for some action. I suppose I must have appeared a strange and enigmatic figure standing there, straight and solemn, surmounted and dominated by the vast cap. But through the mists a flash of insight showed me where I was going wrong. It was over-confidence. It wasn't a bit of good trying to speak loudly like that. I tried again in the faintest of whispers.

'Could I have a bucket of hot water, some soap and a towel, please.' It came out beautifully though the oldest Mr

Bamford didn't quite get it first time. He came close, cupped an ear with his hand and watched my lips intently. Then he nodded eagerly in comprehension, held up a forefinger at me, tiptoed across the floor like a tightrope walker to one of the sons and whispered in his ear. The young man turned and crept out noiselessly, closing the door behind him with the utmost care; he was back in less than a minute, padding over the cobbles daintily in his heavy boots and placing the bucket gingerly in front of me.

I managed to remove my jacket, tie and shirt quite efficiently and they were taken from me in silence and hung up on nails by the Bamfords, who were moving around as though in church. I thought I was doing fine until I started to wash my arms. The soap kept shooting from my arms, slithering into the dung channel, disappearing into the dark corners of the byre with the Bamfords in hot pursuit. It was worse still when I tried to work up to the top of my arms. The soap flew over my shoulders like a live thing, at times cannoning off the walls, at others gliding down my back. The farmers never knew where the next shot was going and they took on the appearance of a really sharp fielding side crouching around me with arms outstretched waiting for a catch.

However, I did finally work up a lather and was ready to start, but the cow refused firmly to get to her feet, so I had to stretch out behind her face down on the unyielding cobbles. It wasn't until I had got down there that I felt the great cap dropping over my ears; I must have put it on again after removing my shirt though it was difficult to see what purpose it might serve.

Inserting a hand gently into the vagina I pushed along the calf's neck, hoping to come upon a flexed knee or even a foot, but I was disappointed; the leg really was right back, stretching from the shoulder away flat against the calf's side. Still, I would be all right – it just meant a longer reach.

And there was one reassuring feature; the calf was alive. As I lay, my face was almost touching the rear end of the cow and I had a close-up of the nose, which kept appearing every few seconds; it was good to see the little nostrils twitching as they sought the outside air. All I had to do was get that leg round.

But the snag was that as I reached forward the cow kept straining, squeezing my arm cruelly against her bony pelvis, making me groan and roll about in agony for a few seconds until the pressure went off. Quite often in these crises my cap fell on to the floor and each time gentle hands replaced it immediately on my head.

At last the foot was in my hand – there would be no need for ropes this time – and I began to pull it round. It took me longer than I thought, and it seemed to me that the calf was beginning to lose patience with me because when its head was forced out by the cow's contractions we were eye to eye and I fancied the little creature was giving me a disgusted 'For heaven's sake get on with it' look.

When the leg did come round it was with a rush and in an instant everything was laid as it should have been.

'Get hold of the feet,' I whispered to the Bamfords and after a hushed consultation they took up their places. In no time at all a fine heifer calf was wriggling on the cobbles, shaking its head and snorting the placental fluid from its nostrils.

In response to my softly hissed instructions the farmers rubbed the little creature down with straw wisps and pulled it round for its mother to lick.

It was a happy ending to the most peaceful calving I have ever attended. Never a voice raised, everybody moving around on tiptoe. I got dressed in a cathedral silence, went out to the car, breathed a final goodnight and left with the Bamfords waving mutely.

To say I had a hangover next morning would be failing even to hint at the utter disintegration of my bodily economy and personality. Only somebody who had consumed two or three quarts of assorted home-made wines at a sitting could have an inkling of the quaking nausea, the raging inferno within, the jangling nerves, the black, despairing outlook.

Tristan had seen me in the bathroom running the cold tap on my tongue and had intuitively administered a raw egg, aspirins and brandy which, as I came downstairs, lay in a cold, unmoving blob in my outraged stomach.

'What are you walking like that for, James?' asked Siegfried in what sounded like a bull's bellow as I came in on him at breakfast. 'You look as though you'd wet yourself.'

'Oh, it's nothing much.' It was no good telling him I was

treading warily across the carpet because I was convinced that if I let my heels down too suddenly it would jar my eyeballs from their sockets. 'I had a few glasses of Mr Crump's wine last night and it seems to have upset me.'

'A few glasses! You ought to be more careful – that stuff's dynamite. Could knock anybody over.' He crashed his cup into its saucer then began to clatter about with knife and fork as if trying to give a one-man rendering of the Anvil Chorus. 'I hope you weren't any the worse to go to Bamford's.'

'Well, I did the job all right, but I'd had a bit too much – no use denying it.'

Siegfried was in one of his encouraging moods. 'By God, James, those Bamfords are very strict Methodists. They're grand chaps but absolutely dead against drink – if they thought you were under the influence of alcohol, they'd never have you on the place again.' He ruthlessly bisected an egg yolk. 'I hope they didn't notice anything. Do you think they knew?'

'Oh, maybe not. No, I shouldn't think so.' I closed my eyes and shivered as Siegfried pushed a forkful of sausage and fried bread into his mouth and began to chew briskly. My mind went back to the gentle hands replacing the monstrous cap on my head, and I groaned inwardly.

Those Bamfords knew all right. Oh, yes, they knew.

The Old Retainers

As I sat at breakfast I looked out at the autumn mist dissolving in the early sunshine. It was going to be another fine day, but there was a chill in the old house this morning, a shiveriness as though a cold hand had reached out to remind us that summer had gone and the hard months lay just ahead.

'It says here,' Siegfried said, adjusting his copy of the *Darrowby and Houlton Times* with care against the coffee-pot, 'that farmers have no feeling for their animals.'

I buttered a piece of toast and looked across at him. 'Cruel, you mean?'

'Well, not exactly, but this chap maintains that to a farmer, livestock are purely commercial – there's no sentiment in his attitude towards them, no affection.'

'Well, it wouldn't do if they were all like poor Kit Bilton, would it? They'd all go mad.'

Kit was a lorry driver who, like so many of the working men of Darrowby, kept a pig at the bottom of his garden for family consumption. The snag was that when killing time came, Kit wept for three days. I happened to go into his house on one of these occasions and found his wife and daughter hard at work cutting up the meat for pies and brawn while Kit huddled miserably by the kitchen fire, his eyes swimming with tears. He was a huge man who could throw a twelve-stone sack of meal on to his wagon with a jerk of his arms, but he seized my hand in his and sobbed at me, 'I can't bear it, Mr Herriot. He was like a Christian was that pig, just like a Christian.'

'No, I agree.' Siegfried leaned over and sawed off a slice of Mrs Hall's home-baked bread. 'But Kit isn't a real farmer. This article is about people who own large numbers of animals. The question is, is it possible for such men to become emotionally involved? Can the dairy farmer milking maybe fifty cows become really fond of any of them, or are they just milk-producing units?'

'It's an interesting point,' I said, 'and I think you've put your finger on it with the numbers. You know, there are a lot of our farmers up in the high country who have only a few stock. They always have names for their cows – Daisy, Mabel, I even came across one called Kipperlugs the other day. I do think these small farmers have an affection for their animals, but I don't see how the big men can possibly have.'

Siegfried rose from the table and stretched luxuriously. 'You're probably right. Anyway, I'm sending you to see a really big man this morning. John Skipton of Dennaby Close – he's got some tooth rasping to do. Couple of old horses losing condition. You'd better take all the instruments; it might be anything.'

I went through to the little room down the passage and surveyed the tooth instruments. I always felt at my most medieval when I was caught up in large-animal dentistry, and in the days of the draught horse it was a regular task. I looked with distaste at the tooth instruments; the vicious forceps with two-feet-long arms, sharp-jawed shears, mouth gags, hammers and chisels, files and rasps; it was rather like a quiet corner in the Spanish Inquisition. We kept a long wooden box with a handle for carrying the things, and I staggered out to the car with a fair selection.

Dennaby Close was not just a substantial farm, it was a monument to a man's endurance and skill. The fine old house, the extensive buildings, the great sweep of lush grass land along the lower slopes of the fell were all proof that old John Skipton had achieved the impossible; he had started as an uneducated farm labourer and he was now a wealthy landowner.

The miracle hadn't happened easily; old John had a lifetime of grinding toil behind him that would have killed most men, a lifetime with no room for a wife or family or creature comforts, but there was more to it than that; there was a brilliant acumen in agricultural matters that had made the old man a legend in the district. 'When all t'world goes one road, I go t'other' was one of his quoted sayings and it is true that the Skipton farms had made money in the hard times when others were going bankrupt. Dennaby was only one of John's farms; he had two large arable places of about four hundred acres each lower down the Dale.

He had conquered, but to some people it seemed that he had himself been conquered in the process. He had battled against the odds for so many years and driven himself so fiercely that he couldn't stop. He could be enjoying all kinds of luxuries now but he just hadn't the time; they said that the poorest of his workers lived in better style than he did.

I paused as I got out of the car and stood gazing at the house as though I had never seen it before; and I marvelled again at the elegance which had withstood over three hundred years of the harsh climate. People came a long way to see Dennaby Close and take photographs of the graceful manor with its tall, leaded windows, the massive chimneys towering over the old moss-grown tiles, or to wander through the neglected garden and climb up the sweep of steps to the entrance with its wide stone arch over the great studded door.

There should have been a beautiful woman in one of those pointed hats peeping out from that mullioned casement or a Cavalier in ruffles and hose pacing beneath the high wall with its pointed copings. But there was just old John stumping impatiently towards me, his tattered, buttonless coat secured only by a length of binder twine round his middle.

'Come in a minute, young man,' he cried. 'I've got a little bill to pay you.' He led the way round to the back of the house and I followed, pondering on the odd fact that it was always a 'little bill' in Yorkshire. We went in through a flagged kitchen to a room which was graceful and spacious but furnished only with a table, a few wooden chairs and a collapsed sofa.

The old man bustled over to the mantelpiece and fished out a bundle of papers from behind the clock. He leafed through them, threw an envelope on to the table, then produced a cheque book and slapped it down in front of me. I did the usual – took out the bill, made out the amount on the cheque and pushed it over for him to sign. He wrote with a careful concentration, the small-featured, weathered face bent low, the peak of the old cloth cap almost touching the pen. His trousers had ridden up his legs as he sat down, showing the skinny calves and bare ankles. There were no socks underneath the heavy boots.

When I had pocketed the cheque, John jumped to his feet. 'We'll have to walk down to t'river; 'osses are down there.' He left the house almost at a trot.

I eased my box of instruments from the car boot. It was a funny thing, but whenever I had heavy equipment to lug about, my patients were always a long way away. This box seemed to be filled with lead, and it wasn't going to get any lighter on the journey down through the walled pastures.

The old man seized a pitchfork, stabbed it into a bale of hay and hoisted it effortlessly over his shoulder. He set off again at the same brisk pace. We made our way down from one gateway to another, often walking diagonally across the fields. John didn't reduce speed and I stumbled after him, puffing a little and trying to put away the thought that he was at least fifty years older than me.

About halfway down we came across a group of men at the age-old task of 'walling' – repairing a gap in one of the dry-stone walls which trace their patterns everywhere on the green slopes of the Dales. One of the men looked up. 'Nice mornin', Mr Skipton,' he sang out cheerfully.

'Bugger t'mornin'. Get on wi' some work,' grunted old John in reply, and the man smiled contentedly as though he had received a compliment.

I was glad when we reached the flat land at the bottom. My arms seemed to have been stretched by several inches and I could feel a trickle of sweat on my brow. Old John appeared unaffected; he flicked the fork from his shoulder and the bale thudded on to the grass.

The two horses turned towards us at the sound. They were standing fetlock-deep in the pebbly shallows just beyond a little beach which merged into the green carpet of turf; nose to tail, they had been rubbing their chins gently along each other's backs, unconscious of our approach. A high cliff overhanging the far bank made a perfect windbreak while on either side of us clumps of oak and beech blazed in the autumn sunshine.

'They're in a nice spot, Mr Skipton,' I said.

'Aye, they can keep cool in the hot weather and they've got the barn when winter comes.' John pointed to a low, thick-walled building with a single door. 'They can come and go as they please.'

The sound of his voice brought the horses out of the river at a stiff trot, and as they came near you could see they really were old. The mare was a chestnut and the gelding was a light bay, but their coats were so flecked with grey that they almost looked like roans. This was most pronounced on their faces where the sprinkling of white hairs, the sunken eyes and the deep cavity above the eyes gave them a truly venerable appearance.

For all that, they capered around John with a fair attempt at skittishness, stamping their feet, throwing their heads about, pushing his cap over his eyes with their muzzles.

'Get by, leave off!' he shouted. 'Daft awd beggars.' But he tugged absently at the mare's forelock and ran his hand briefly along the neck of the gelding.

'When did they last do any work ?' I asked.

'Oh, about twelve years ago, I reckon.'

I stared at John. 'Twelve years! And have they been down here all that time?'

'Aye, just larkin' about down here, retired like. They've earned it an' all.' For a few moments he stood silent, shoulders hunched, hands deep in the pockets of his coat, then he spoke quietly as if to himself. 'They were two slaves when I was a slave.' He turned and looked at me and for a revealing moment I read in the pale-blue eyes something of the agony and struggle he had shared with the animals.

'But twelve years! How old are they, anyway?'

John's mouth twisted up at one corner. 'Well you're t'vet. You tell me.'

I stepped forward confidently, my mind buzzing with Galvayne's groove, shape of marks, degree of slope and the rest; I grasped the unprotesting upper lip of the mare and looked at her teeth.

 'Good God!' I gasped. 'I've never seen anything like this.'

The incisors were immensely long and projecting forward until they met at an angle of about forty-five degrees. There were no marks at all – they had long since gone.

I laughed and turned back to the old man. 'It's no good, I'd only be guessing. You'll have to tell me.'

'Well she's about thirty and gelding's a year or two younger. She's had fifteen grand foals and never ailed owt except a bit of teeth trouble. We've had them rasped a time or two and it's time they were done again, I reckon. They're both losing condition and dropping bits of half-chewed hay from their mouths. Gelding's the worst – has a right job champin' his grub.'

I put my hand into the mare's mouth, grasped her tongue and pulled it out to one side. A quick exploration of the molars with my other hand revealed what I suspected; the outside edges of the upper teeth were overgrown and jagged and were irritating the cheeks while the inside edges of the lower molars were in a similar state and were making the tongue sore.

'I'll soon make her more comfortable, Mr Skipton. With those sharp edges rubbed off she'll be as good as new.' I got the rasp out of my vast box, held the tongue in one hand and worked the rough surface along the teeth, checking occasionally with my fingers until the points had been sufficiently reduced.

'That's about right,' I said after a few minutes. 'I don't want to make them too smooth or she won't be able to grind her food.'

John grunted. 'Good enough. Now have a look at t'other. There's summat far wrong with him.'

I had a feel at the gelding's teeth. 'Just the same as the mare. Soon put him right, too.'

But pushing at the rasp, I had an uncomfortable feeling that something was not quite right. The thing wouldn't go fully to the back of the mouth; something was stopping it. I stopped rasping and explored again, reaching with my fingers as far as I could. And I came upon something very strange, something which shouldn't have been there at all. It was like a great chunk of bone projecting down from the roof of the mouth.

It was time I had a proper look. I got out my pocket torch and shone it over the back of the tongue. It was easy to see the trouble now; the last dipper molar was overlapping the lower one, resulting in a gross overgrowth. The result was a sabre-like barb about three inches long stabbing down into the tender tissue of the gum.

That would have to come off – right now. My jauntiness vanished and I suppressed a shudder; it meant using the horrible shears – those great long-handled things with the screw operated by a crossbar. They gave me the willies because I am one of those people who can't bear to watch anybody blowing up a balloon and this was the same sort of thing only worse. You fastened the sharp blades of the shears on to the tooth and began to turn the bar slowly, slowly. Soon the tooth began to groan and creak under the tremendous leverage and you knew that any second it would break off and when it did it was like somebody letting off a rifle in your ear. That was when all hell usually broke loose, but mercifully this was a quiet old horse and I hoped he wouldn't start dancing around on his hind legs. There was no pain for the horse because the overgrown part had no nerve supply – it was the noise that caused the trouble.

Returning to my crate, I produced the dreadful instrument and with it a gag, which I inserted on the incisors and opened on its ratchet until the mouth gaped wide. Everything was easy to see then and, of course, there it was – a great prong at the other side of the mouth exactly like the first. Great, great, now I had two to chop off.

The old horse stood patiently, eyes almost closed, as though he had seen it all and nothing in the world was going to bother him. I went through the motions with my toes curling and when the sharp crack came, the white-bordered eyes opened wide, but only in mild surprise. He never even moved. When I did the other side he paid no attention at all; in fact, with the gag prising his jaws apart he looked exactly as though he were yawning with boredom.

As I bundled the tools away, John picked up the bony spicules from the grass and studied them with interest. 'Well, poor awd beggar. Good job I got you along, young man. Reckon he'll feel a lot better now.'

On the way back, old John, relieved of his bale, was able to go twice as fast and he stumped his way up the hill at a furious pace, using the fork as a staff. I panted along in the rear, changing the box from hand to hand every few minutes.

About halfway up, the thing slipped out of my grasp and it gave me a chance to stop for a breather. As the old man muttered impatiently, I looked back and could just see the two horses; they had returned to the shallows and were playing together, chasing each other jerkily, their feet splashing in the water. The cliff made a dark backcloth to the picture – the shining river, the trees glowing bronze and gold and the sweet green of the grass.

Back in the farmyard, John paused awkwardly. He nodded once or twice, said, 'Thank ye, young man,' then turned abruptly and walked away.

I was dumping the box thankfully into the boot when I saw the man who had spoken to us on the way down. He was sitting, cheerful as ever, in a sunny corner, back against a pile of sacks, pulling his dinner packet from an old army satchel.

'You've been down to see t'pensioners, then? By gaw, awd John should know the way.'

'Regular visitor, is he?'

'Regular? Every day God sends you'll see t'awd feller ploddin' down there. Rain, snow or blow, never misses. And allus has summat with him – bag o' corn, straw for their bedding.'

'And he's done that for twelve years?'

The man unscrewed his thermos flask and poured himself a cup of black tea. 'Aye, them 'osses haven't done a stroke o' work all that time. Rum 'un, isn't it?'

'You're right,' I said, 'it is a rum 'un.'

 Just how rum it was occupied my thoughts on the way

back to the surgery. I went back to my conversation with Siegfried that morning; we had just about decided that the man with a lot of animals couldn't be expected to feel affection for individuals among them But those buildings back there were full of John Skipton's animals – he must have had hundreds.

Yet what made him trail down that hillside every day in all weathers? Why had he filled the last years of those two old horses with peace and beauty? Why had he given them a final ease and comfort which he had withheld from himself?

It could only be love.

A Case of Poisoning

There is no doubt that when I looked back at my life in Darrowby I was inclined to bathe the whole thing in a rosy glow, but occasionally the unhappy things came to mind.

That man, distraught and gasping on the surgery steps. 'I's no good, I can't bring him in. He's as stiff as a board!'

My stomach lurched. It was another one. 'Jasper, you mean?'

'Yes, he's in the back of my car, right here.'

I ran across the pavement and opened the car door. It was as I feared; a handsome Dalmatian stretched in a dreadful tetanic spasm, spine arched, head craning desperately backward, legs like four wooden rods groping at nothing.

I didn't wait to talk but dashed back into the house for syringe and drugs.

I leaned into the car, tucked some papers under the dog's head, gave the injection and waited.

The man looked at me with anxious eyes. 'What is it?'

'Strychnine poisoning, Mr Bartle. I've just given an emetic to make him vomit.' As I spoke the animal brought up the contents of his stomach on to the paper.

'Will that put him right?'

'It depends on how much of the poison has been absorbed.' I didn't feel like telling him that it was almost invariably fatal, that in fact I had treated six dogs in the last week with the same condition and they had all died. 'We'll just have to hope.'

He watched me as I filled another syringe with barbiturate. 'What are you doing now?'

'Anaesthetizing him.' I slipped the needle into the radial vein and as I slowly trickled the fluid into the dog's bloodstream the taut muscles relaxed and he sank into a deep slumber.

'He looks better already,' Mr Bartle said.

'Yes, but the trouble is when the injection wears off he may go back into a spasm. As I say, it all depends on how much of the strychnine has got into his system. Keep him in a quiet place with as little noise as possible. Any sound can bring on a spasm. When he shows signs of coming out of it give me a ring.'

I went back into the house. Seven cases in a week! It was tragic and scarcely believable, but there was no doubt left in my mind now. This was malicious. Some psychopath in our little town was deliberately putting down poison to kill dogs. Strychnine poisoning was something that cropped up occasionally. Gamekeepers and other people used the deadly drug to kill vermin, but usually it was handled with great care and placed out of reach of domestic pets. Trouble started when a burrowing dog came across the poison by accident. But this was different.

I had to warn pet owners somehow. I lifted the telephone and spoke to one of the reporters on the *Darrowby and*

Houlton Times. He promised to put the story in the next edition, along with advice to keep dogs on their leads and otherwise supervise pets more carefully.

Then I rang the police. The sergeant listened to my account. 'Right, Mr Herriot. I agree with you that there's some crackpot going around and we'll certainly investigate this matter. If you'll just give me the names of the dog owners involved . . . thank you . . . thank you. We'll see these people and check round the local chemists to see if anybody has been buying strychnine lately. And, of course, we'll keep our eyes open for anybody acting suspiciously.'

I came away from the telephone feeling that I might have done something to halt the depressing series of events, but I couldn't rid myself of a gloomy apprehension that more trouble was round the corner. But my mood lightened when I saw Johnny Clifford in the waiting-room.

Johnny always made me feel better because he was invariably optimistic and wore a cheerful grin which never altered, even though he was blind. He was about my own age and he sat there in his habitual pose, one hand on the head of his guide dog, Fergus.

'Is it inspection time again already, Johnny?' I asked.

'Aye, it is that, Mr Herriot, it's come round again. It's been a quick six months.' He laughed and held out his card.

I squatted and looked into the face of the big Alsatian sitting motionless and dignified by his master's side. 'Well, and how's Fergus these days?'

'Oh, he's in grand fettle. Eatin' well and full of life.' The hand on the head moved round to the ears and at the other end the tail did a bit of sweeping along the waiting-room floor.

As I looked at the young man, his face alight with pride and affection, I realized afresh what this dog meant to him. He had told me that when his failing sight progressed to total blindness in his early twenties he was filled with a despair which did not lessen until he was sent to train with a guide dog and met Fergus, because he found something more than another living creature to act as his eyes, he found a friend and companion to share every moment of his days.

'Well, we'd better get started,' I said. 'Stand up a minute, old lad, while I take your temperature.' That was normal and I went over the big animal's chest with a stethoscope, listening to the reassuringly steady thud of the heart. As I parted the hair along the neck and back to examine the skin I laughed.

'I'm wasting my time here, Johnny. You've got his coat in perfect condition.'

'Aye, never a day goes by but he gets a good groomin'.'

I had seen him at it, brushing and combing tirelessly to bring extra lustre to the sleek swathes of hair. The nicest thing anybody could say to Johnny was, 'That's a beautiful dog you've got.' His pride in that beauty was boundless, even though he had never seen it himself.

Treating guide dogs for the blind has always seemed to me to be one of a veterinary surgeon's most rewarding tasks. To be in a position to help and care for these magnificent animals is a privilege, not just because they are highly trained and valuable but because they represent, in the ultimate way, something which has always lain near the core and centre of my life: the mutually depending, trusting and loving association between man and animal.

Meeting these blind people was a humbling experience which sent me about my work with a new appreciation of my blessings.

I opened the dog's mouth and peered at the huge, gleaming teeth. It was dicing with danger to do this with some Alsatians, but with Fergus you could haul the great jaws apart and nearly put your head in and he would only lick your ear. In fact, he was at it now. My cheek was nicely within range and he gave it a quick wipe with his large wet tongue.

'Hey, just a minute, Fergus!' I withdrew and plied my handkerchief. 'I've had a wash this morning. And anyway, only little dogs lick – not big tough Alsatians.'

Johnny threw back his head and gave a great peal of laughter. 'There's nowt tough about him, he's the softest dog you could ever meet.'

'Well, that's the way I like them,' I said. I reached for a tooth scaler. 'There's just a bit of tartar on one of his back teeth. I'll scrape it off right now.'

When I had finished I looked in the ears; there was no canker but I cleaned out a little wax. Then I went round the feet, examining paws and claws. They always fascinated me, these feet; wide, enormous, with great spreading toes. They had to be that size to support the big body and the massive bones of the limbs.

'All correct except that one funny claw, Johnny.'

'Aye, you allus have to trim that 'un, don't you? I could feel it was growin' long again.'

'Yes, that toe seems to be slightly crooked or it would wear down like the others with all the walking he does. You have a great time going walks all day, don't you, Fergus?'

I dodged another attempted lick and closed my clippers around the claw. I had to squeeze until my eyes popped before the overgrown piece shot away with a loud crack.

'By gosh, we'd go through some clippers if all dogs had claws like that,' I gasped. 'It just about does them in every time he calls.'

Johnny laughed again and dropped his hand on the great head with that gesture which said so much.

I took the card and entered my report on the dog's health along with the things I had done. Then I dated it and handed it back. 'That's it for this time, Johnny. He's in excellent order and there's nothing more I need do to him.'

'Thank you, Mr Herriot. See you next time round, then.' The young man took hold of the harness and I followed the two of them along the passage and out of the front door. I watched as Fergus halted by the kerb and waited until a car had passed before crossing the road.

They hadn't gone very far along the road when a woman with a shopping bag stopped them. She began to chatter animatedly, looking down repeatedly at the big dog. She was talking about Fergus and Johnny rested his hand on the noble head and nodded and smiled. Fergus was his favourite topic.

Shortly after midday Mr Bartle rang to say Jasper showed signs of returning spasms and before sitting down to lunch I rushed round to his house and repeated the barbiturate injection. Mr Bartle owned one of the local mills, producing cattle food for the district. He was a very bright man indeed.

'Mr Herriot,' he said, 'please don't misunderstand me. I have every faith in you, but isn't there anything else you can do? I am so very fond of this dog.'

I shrugged helplessly. 'I'm sorry, but I can't do any more.'

'But is there no antidote to this poison?'

'No, I'm afraid there isn't.'

'Well . . .' He looked down with drawn face at the unconscious animal. 'What's going on? What's happening to Jasper when he goes stiff like he did? I'm only a layman but I like to understand things.'

'I'll try to explain it,' I said. 'Strychnine is absorbed into the nervous system and it increases the conductivity of the spinal cord.'

'What does that mean?'

'It means that the muscles become more sensitive to outside stimuli so that the slightest touch or sound throws them into violent contractions.'

'But why does a dog stretch out like that?'

'Because the extensor muscles are stronger than the flexors, causing the back to be arched and the legs extended.'

He nodded. 'I see, but . . . I believe it is usually fatal. What is it that . . . that kills them?'

'They die of asphyxia due to paralysis of the respiratory centre or contraction of the diaphragm.'

Maybe he wanted to ask more, but it was painful for him and he stayed silent.

'There's one thing I'd like you to know, Mr Bartle,' I said. 'It is almost certainly not a painful condition.'

'Thank you.' He bent and briefly stroked the sleeping dog. 'So nothing more can be done?'

I shook my head. 'The barbiturate keeps the spasms in abeyance and we'll go on hoping he hasn't absorbed too much strychnine. I'll call back later, or you can ring me if he gets worse. I can be here in a few minutes.'

Driving away, I pondered on the irony that made Darrowby a paradise for dog killers as well as dog lovers. There were grassy tracks everywhere; wandering by the river's edge, climbing the fellsides and coiling green and tempting among the heather on the high tops. I often felt sympathy for pet owners in the big cities, trying to find places to walk their dogs. Here in Darrowby we could take our pick. But so could the poisoner. He could drop his deadly bait unobserved in a hundred different places.

I was finishing the afternoon surgery when the telephone rang. It was Mr Bartle.

'Has he started the spasms again?' I asked.

There was a pause. 'No, I'm afraid Jasper is dead. He never regained consciousness.'

'Oh . . . I'm very sorry.' I felt a dull despair. That was the seventh death in a week.

'Well, thank you for your treatment, Mr Herriot. I'm sure nothing could have saved him.'

I hung up the phone wearily. He was right. Nothing or nobody could have done any good in this case, but it didn't help. If you finish up with a dead animal, there is always the feeling of defeat.

Next day I had just driven into a farm when the farmer's wife called to me. 'I have a message for you to ring back to the surgery.'

I heard Helen's voice at the other end. 'Jack Brimham has just come in with his dog. I think it's another strychnine case.'

I excused myself and drove back to Darrowby at top speed. Jack Brimham was a builder. He ran a one-man business and whatever job he was on – repairing roofs or walls or chimneys – his little white rough-haired terrier went with him, and you could usually see the little animal nosing among the piles of bricks, exploring in the surrounding fields.

Jack was a friend, too. I often had a beer with him at the Drovers' Arms, and I recognized his van outside the surgery. I went along the passage and found him leaning over the table in the consulting room. His dog was stretched there in that attitude which I dreaded.

'He's gone, Jim,' he muttered.

I looked at the shaggy little body. There was no movement,

the eyes stared silently. The legs, even in death, strained across the smooth surface of the table. It was pointless, but I slipped my hand inside the thigh and felt for the femoral artery. There was no pulse.

'I'm sorry, Jack,' I said.

He didn't answer for a moment. 'I've been readin' about this in the paper, Jim, but I never thought it would happen to me. It's a bugger, isn't it?'

I nodded. He was a craggy-faced man, a tough Yorkshireman with a humour and integrity which I liked and a soft place inside which his dog had occupied. I did not know what to say to him.

'Who's doin' this?' he said, half to himself.

'I don't know, Jack. Nobody knows.'

'Well, I wish I could have five minutes with him, that's all.' He gathered the rigid little form into his arms and went out.

My troubles were not over for that day. It was about 11 p.m. and I had just got into bed when Helen nudged me.

'I think there's somebody knocking at the front door, Jim.'

I opened the window and looked out. Old Boardman, the lame veteran of the first war who did odd jobs for us, was standing on the steps.

'Mr Herriot,' he called up to me. 'I'm sorry to bother you at this hour, but Patch is ill.'

I leaned further out. 'What's he doing?'

'He's like a bit o' wood – stiff like, and laid on 'is side.'

I didn't bother to dress, just pulled my working corduroys

over my pyjamas and went down the stairs two at a time. I grabbed what I needed from the dispensary and opened the front door. The old man, in shirt sleeves, caught at my arm.

'Come quickly, Mr Herriot!' He limped ahead of me to his little house about twenty yards away in the lane round the corner.

Patch was like all the others. The fat spaniel I had seen so often waddling round the top yard with his master was in that nightmare position on the kitchen floor, but he had vomited, which gave me hope. I administered the intravenous injection but as I withdrew the needle the breathing stopped.

Mrs Boardman, in nightgown and slippers, dropped on her knees and stretched a trembling hand towards the motionless animal.

'Patch . . .' She turned and stared at me, wide-eyed. 'He's dead!'

I put my hand on the old woman's shoulder and said some sympathetic words. I thought grimly that I was getting good at it. As I left I looked back at the two old people. Boardman was kneeling now by his wife and even after I had closed the door I could hear their voices: 'Patch . . . Oh, Patch.'

I almost reeled over the few steps to Skeldale House and before going in I stood in the empty street breathing the cool air and trying to calm my racing thoughts. With Patch gone, this thing was getting very near home. I saw that dog every day. In fact, all the dogs that had died were old friends – in a little town like Darrowby you came to know your patients personally. Where was it going to end?

I didn't sleep much that night and over the next few days I was obsessed with apprehension. I expected another poisoning with every phone call and took care never to let my own dog, Sam, out of the car in the region of the town. Thanks to my job, I was able to exercise him miles away on the summits of the fells, but even there I kept him close to me.

By the fourth day I was beginning to feel more relaxed. Maybe the nightmare was over. I was driving home in the late afternoon past the row of grey cottages at the end of the Houlton Road when a woman ran waving into the road.

'Oh, Mr Herriot,' she cried when I stopped. 'I was just goin' to t'phone box when I saw you.'

I pulled up by the kerb. 'It's Mrs Clifford, isn't it?'

'Yes, Johnny's just come in and Fergus 'as gone queer. Collapsed and laid on t'floor.'

'Oh, no!' An icy chill drove through me and for a moment I stared at her, unable to move. Then I threw open the car door and hurried after Johnny's mother into the end cottage. I halted abruptly in the little room and stared down in horror. The very sight of the splendid dignified animal scrabbling helplessly on the linoleum was a desecration, but strychnine is no respecter of such things.

'Oh, God!' I breathed. 'Has he vomited, Johnny?'

'Aye, me mum said he was sick in t'back garden when we came in.' The young man was sitting very upright in a chair by the side of his dog. Even now there was a half-smile on his face, but he looked strained as he put out his hand in the old gesture and failed to find the head that should have been there.

The bottle of barbiturate wobbled in my shaking hand as I filled the syringe. I tried to put away the thought that I was doing what I had done to all the others – all the dead ones. At my feet Fergus panted desperately, then as I bent over him he suddenly became still and went into the horrible distinctive spasm, the great limbs I knew so well straining frantically into space, the head pulled back grotesquely over the spine.

This was when they died, when the muscles were at full contraction. As the barbiturate flowed into the vein I waited for signs of relaxation but saw none. Fergus was about twice as heavy as any of the other victims I had treated and the plunger went to the end of the syringe without result.

Quickly I drew in another dose and began to inject it, my tension building as I saw how much I was administering. The recommended dose was 1 cc per 5 lb body weight and beyond that you could kill the animal. I watched the gradations on the glass barrel of the syringe and my mouth went dry when the dose crept far beyond the safety limit. But I knew I had to relieve this spasm and continued to depress the plunger relentlessly.

I did it in the grim knowledge that if he died now, I would never know whether to blame the strychnine or myself for his death.

The big dog had received more than a lethal amount before peace began to return to the taut body and even then I sat back on my heels, almost afraid to look in case I had brought about his end. There was a long, agonizing moment when he lay still and apparently lifeless, then the rib cage began to move almost imperceptibly as the breathing recommenced.

Even then I was in suspense. The anaesthesia was so deep that he was only just alive, yet I knew that the only hope was to keep him that way. I sent Mrs Clifford out to phone Siegfried to say that I would be tied up here for a while, then I pulled up a chair and settled down to wait.

The hours passed as Johnny and I sat there, the dog stretched between us. The young man discussed the case calmly and without self-pity. There was no suggestion that this was anything more than a pet animal lying at his feet – except for the tell-tale reaching for the head that was no longer there.

Several times Fergus showed signs of going into another spasm and each time I sent him back into his deep, deep insensibility, pushing him repeatedly to the brink with a fateful certainty that it was the only way.

It was well after midnight when I came sleepily out into the darkness. I felt drained. Watching the life of the friendly, clever, face-licking animal flicker as he lay inert and unheeding had been a tremendous strain, but I had left him sleeping – still anaesthetized but breathing deeply and regularly. Would he wake up and start the dread sequence again? I didn't know, but I couldn't stay any longer. There was a practice with other animals to attend to.

But my anxiety jerked me into early wakefulness next morning. I tossed around till seven thirty, telling myself this wasn't the way to be a veterinary surgeon, that you couldn't live like this. But my worry was stronger than the voice of reason and I slipped out before breakfast to the roadside cottage.

My nerves were like a bowstring as I knocked on the door. Mrs Clifford answered and I was about to blurt out my inquiries when Fergus trotted from the inner room.

He was still a little groggy from the vast dosage of barbiturate, but he was relaxed and happy. The symptoms had gone. He was himself again. With a gush of pure joy I knelt and took the great head between my hands. He slobbered at me playfully with his wet tongue and I had to fight him off.

He followed me into the living-room where Johnny was seated at the table, drinking tea. He took up his usual position, sitting upright and proud by his master's side.

'You'll have a cup, Mr Herriot?' Mrs Clifford asked, poising the teapot.

'Thanks, I'd love one, Mrs Clifford,' I replied.

No tea ever tasted better, and as I sipped I watched the young man's smiling face.

'What a relief, Mr Herriot! I sat up with him all night, listenin' to the chimes of the church clock. It was just after four when I knew we'd won because I heard 'im get to his feet and sort o' stagger about. I stopped worryin' then, just listened to 'is feet patterin' on the linoleum. It was lovely!'

He turned his head to me and I looked at the slightly upturned eyes in the cheerful face.

'I'd have been lost without Fergus,' he said softly. 'I don't know how to thank you.'

But as he unthinkingly rested his hand on the head of the big dog who was his pride and delight I felt that the gesture alone was all the thanks I wanted.

That was the end of the strychnine poisoning outbreak in Darrowby. The older people still talk about it, but nobody ever had the slightest clue to the identity of the killer, and it is a mystery to this day.

I feel that the vigilance of the police and the publicity in the press frightened this twisted person off, but anyway it just stopped and the only cases since then have been accidental ones.

To me it is a sad memory of failure and frustration. Fergus was my only cure and I'm not sure why he recovered. Maybe the fact that I pushed the injection to dangerous levels because I was desperate had something to do with it, or maybe he just didn't pick up as much poison as the others. I'll never know.

But over the years when I saw the big dog striding majestically in his harness, leading his master unerringly around the streets of Darrowby, I always had the same feeling.

If there had to be just one saved, I'm glad it was him.

There's Soap – and Soap

Five o'clock in the morning and the telephone jangling in my ear. Ewe lambing at Walton's, a lonely farm on the high moorland, and as I crawled from the haven of bed into the icy air of the bedroom and began to pull on my clothes, I tried not to think of the comfortless hour or two ahead.

Pushing my arms through my shirt sleeves, I gritted my teeth as the cloth chafed the flesh. In the pale dawn light I could see the little red fissures which covered my hands and ran up to my elbows. In lambing time I hardly ever seemed to have my jacket on and the constant washing in the open pens or in windy fields had turned my skin to raw meat. I could detect the faint scent of Helen's glycerine and rose water which she applied to my arms every night to make them bearable.

Helen stirred under the blankets and I went over and kissed her cheek. 'Off to Walton's,' I whispered.

Eyes closed, she nodded against the pillow, and I could just hear her sleepy murmur. 'Yes . . . I heard.'

Going out of the door I looked back at my wife's huddled bulk. When this happened she too was jerked into the world of work and duty. That phone could blast off again at any time and she would have to get in touch with me. And on top of this she would have to get the fires lit, the tea made and the children started with their breakfast – the little tasks I tried to help her with and which weren't easy in our big, beautiful icebox of a house.

Through the tight-shut, sleeping little town, then on to the narrow road winding between its walls until the trees dwindled and disappeared, leaving the wide, windswept fells bare and unwelcoming at this hour.

I wondered if there was any chance of the ewe being under cover. In the early fifties, it didn't seem to occur to many of the farmers to bring their lambing ewes into the buildings, and I attended to the great majority out in the open fields. There were happy times when I almost chuckled in relief at the sight of a row of hurdles in a warm fold yard, or sometimes the farmers would build pens from stacked-up straw bales, but on this occasion my spirits plummeted when I drew up at the farm and met Mr Walton, who came out of the house carrying a bucket of water and headed for the gate.

'Outside, is she?' I asked, trying to sound airy.

'Aye, just ower there.' He pointed over the long, bracken-splashed pasture to a prone woolly form in the distance, which looked a hell of a long way 'ower there'. As I trailed across the frosty grass, my medical bag and obstetric overall dangling, a merciless wind tore at me, picking up an extra Siberian cold from the long drifts of snow which still lay behind the walls in this late Yorkshire spring.

As I stripped off and knelt behind the ewe I looked around. We were right on top of the world and the panorama of hills and valleys with grey farmhouses and pebbled rivers in their depths was beautiful but would have been more inviting if it had been a warm summer afternoon and I had been preparing for a picnic with my family.

I held out my hand and the farmer deposited a tiny sliver of soap on my palm. I always felt that farmers kept special pieces of soap for the vet – minute portions of scrubbing soap which were too small and hard to be of any use. I rubbed this piece frantically with my hands, dipping frequently into the water, but I could work up only the most meagre film of lather. Not enough to protect my tender arm as I inserted it into the ewe, and the farmer looked at me inquiringly as I softly ooh'd and aah'd my way towards the cervix.

I found just what I didn't want to find. A big single lamb, jammed tight. Two lambs are the norm and three quite common, but a big single lamb often spells trouble. It was one of my joys in practice to sort out the tangles of twins and triplets, but with the singles it was a case of not enough room and the big lamb had to be eased and pulled out as gently as possible – a long and tedious business.

Resigning myself to the fact that I was going to spend a long time crouched on that windy hilltop, I reached as far as possible and poked a finger into the lamb's mouth, feeling a surge of relief as the little tongue stirred against my hand. He was alive, anyway, and with a lifting of my spirits I began the familiar ritual of introducing lubricating jelly, locating the tiny legs and fastening them with snares and, finally, as I sat back on my heels for a breather I knew that all I had to do now was to bring the head through the pelvis. That was the tricky bit. If it came through I was home and dry; if it didn't I was in trouble. Mr Walton, holding back the wool from the vulva, watched me in silence. Despite his lifetime experience with sheep he was helpless in a case like this because, like most farmers, he had huge, work-roughened hands with fingers like bananas and could not possibly have got inside a ewe. My small 'lady's hand' as they called it was a blessing.

I hooked my forefinger into the eye socket – my favourite trick, there was nothing else to get hold of except the lower jaw, which was dangerously fragile – and began to pull with infinite care. The ewe strained, crushing my hand against the pelvic bones – not as bad as in a cow but painful, and my mouth opened wide as I eased and twisted and pulled until, with a blessed surge, the head slipped through the bony pelvic opening.

It wasn't long, then, until feet, legs and nose appeared at the vulva and I brought the little creature out on to the grass. He lay still for a moment, snuffling at the cold world he had entered, then he shook his head vigorously. I smiled. That was the best sign of all.

I had another wrestle with the morsel of soap, then the farmer wordlessly handed me a piece of sacking to dry my arms. This was quite common in those days. Towels were scarce commodities on the farms, and I couldn't blame the farmers' wives for hesitating to send out a clean towel to a man who had just had his arms up the back end of an animal. An old soiled one was the usual and, if not, the hessian sack was always at hand. I couldn't rub my painful arms with the coarse material and contented myself with a careful patting, before pushing them, still damp, into the sleeves of my jacket.

The ewe, hearing a high-pitched call from her lamb, began to talk back with the soft deep baa I knew so well, and as she got up and began an intensive licking of the little creature I stood there, forgetful of the cold, listening to their conversation, enthralled as ever by the miracle of birth. When the lamb, apparently feeling he was wasting time, struggled to his feet and tottered unsteadily round to the milk bar I grinned in satisfaction and made my way back to the car.

After breakfast, my next call was to a 'cleansing', the removal of the afterbirth from a cow, and again, after a struggle with a rock-hard marble of soap, I was offered a sack to dry myself, only this time it had recently contained potatoes and I found I was powdering my chapped arms with soil. Later that morning, after another calving, I had the choice of a truly filthy 'cow house towel' which must have had an astronomical bacterial count and declined it in favour of yet another piece of hessian.

My arms were red-hot inside my sleeves when I drove into the Birrell farmyard, but I knew better things awaited me here. Wonderful things, in fact.

I never knew what George Birrell's attitude to towels might be or that of his wife, but his mother, old Grandma Birrell, had very clear views on the matter. When I had finished stitching a tear on a cow's udder I stood on the cobbles, blood-spattered and expectant, waiting for the old lady. Right on cue, she came into the byre, hand in hand with four-year-old Lucy, the youngest of her grandchildren. She set down a milking stool and laid out, in a perfectly folded oblong, a newly laundered towel of snowy whiteness; on top of this she placed a tablet of expensive lavender toilet soap in its wrappings, virgin and unopened. A brightly scoured aluminium bucket of steaming water completed the picture, as pretty a one as ever I had seen.

Reverently I peeled the paper from the soap – it was always a new tablet – and as I dipped into the water and spread the rich lather on my burning arms, inhaling the fragrance of the lavender, I almost crooned with ecstasy. The farmer stood by impassively with perhaps the faintest twitch of amusement round his mouth, but Grandma Birrell and Lucy watched my ablutions with rapt enjoyment.

It was always like this at the Birrells', and I loved it, but I could never quite understand why it happened. Maybe Siegfried had a point when he said that old ladies liked me, and he was always pulling my leg about my 'harem' of over-seventies who insisted I should attend their dogs. Anyway, whatever the cause, I revelled in the patronage of Grandma Birrell. In her eyes, everything had to be right for me. Nothing was too good for Mr Herriot.

It was a Saturday morning when Siegfried pushed the *Darrowby and Houlton Times* across the office desk to me.

'Bit of sad news for you, I'm afraid, James,' he murmured, pointing to an entry.

It was in the deaths column. 'Mrs Marjorie Birrell, aged 78, dearly beloved wife of the late Herbert Birrell . . .' I read it through with a growing sense of loss, a rising wistfulness at the feeling of something good coming to an end.

Siegfried gave me a lopsided smile. 'Your old clean-towel friend, eh?'

'That's right.' Her clean towels were her expression of friendship, and it was as a friend I would always remember her. In my mind's eye, I could see her plainly in her flowered apron, standing by the milking stool with Lucy. She was of the farming generation which had come through the tough times before the war, and her gaunt, slightly bowed frame and lined face bore testimony to the hard years. It was the kind of face I had seen on so many of the old Yorkshire folk – grim, but kindly. I knew I was going to miss her.

Just how much I would miss her came to me forcibly on my next visit to the Birrell farm. As I finished my job I looked at my soiled hands with the renewed pang of realization that the old lady wouldn't be coming through that door. I knew George Birrell wouldn't offer me a sack, but what was going to happen?

As I pondered, the half-door was pushed open and little Lucy came into the byre, staggering slightly as she carried the familiar shining bucket of hot water. Then from under her arm she produced a towel and soap and laid them on a milking stool. And it was the same spotless, geometrically folded towel and the same pristine toilet soap as before.

Slightly flushed, the little girl looked up at me. 'Gran said I had to look after you,' she said breathlessly. 'She told me what to do.'

I swallowed a big lump. 'Well, Lucy . . . that's wonderful. And you've done everything just right.'

She nodded, well pleased, and I stole a look at her father, standing there, leaning on a cow. But George's face was inscrutable.

I peeled the wrapper from the soap and began to wash, and as the scent of the lavender rose around me I was carried back to all the other days.

I lathered my hands in silence, then the little girl spoke again. 'Mr Herriot, the only thing is, I'm five now and I'll soon be goin' to school. I don't know how you're goin' to manage.'

I didn't know what to say, but her father broke in.

'Don't worry, luv,' he said. 'I'll do me best if you'll teach me how, and anyway, from now on I'm goin' to try to call Mr Herriot out only on Saturdays.'

The Little Incidents of Life

It looked as though I was going to make it back to the road all right. And I was thankful for it because seven o'clock in the morning, with the wintry dawn only just beginning to lighten the eastern rim of the moor, was no time to be digging my car out of the snow.

This narrow, unfenced road skirted a high tableland and gave on to a few lonely farms at the end of even narrower tracks. It hadn't actually been snowing on my way out to this early call – a uterine haemorrhage in a cow – but the wind had been rising steadily and whipping the top surface from the white blanket which had covered the fell-tops for weeks. My headlights had picked out the creeping drifts; pretty, pointed fingers feeling their way, inch by inch, across the strip of tarmac.

This was how all blocked roads began, and at the farm as I attended to my patient I could hear the wind buffeting the byre door and wondered if I would win the race home.

On the way back the drifts had stopped being pretty and lay across the road like white bolsters, but my little car had managed to cleave through them, veering crazily at times, wheels spinning, and now I could see the main road a few hundred yards ahead, reassuringly black in the pale light.

But just over there on the left, a field away, was Cote

House. I was treating a bullock there – he had eaten some frozen turnips – and a visit was fixed for today. I didn't fancy trailing back up here if I could avoid it, and there was a light in the kitchen window. The family were up, anyway. I turned and drove down into the yard.

The farmhouse door lay within a small porch and the wind had driven the snow inside forming a smooth, two-foot heap against the timbers. As I leaned across to knock, the surface of the heap trembled a little, then began to heave. There was something in there, something quite big. It was eerie standing in the half-light watching the snow parting to reveal a furry body. Some creature of the wild must have strayed in, searching for warmth – but it was bigger than a fox or anything else I could think of.

Just then the door opened and the light from the kitchen streamed out. Peter Trenholm beckoned me inside and his wife smiled at me from the bright interior. They were a cheerful young couple.

'What's that?' I gasped, pointing at the animal, which was shaking the snow vigorously from its coat.

'That?' Peter grinned. 'That's awd Tip.'

'Tip? Your dog? But what's he doing under a pile of snow?'

'Just blew in on him, I reckon. That's where he sleeps, you know, just outside back door.'

I stared at the farmer. 'You mean he sleeps there, out in the open, every night?'

'Aye, allus. Summer and winter. But don't look at me like

that, Mr Herriot – it's his own choice. The other dogs have a warm bed in the cow house, but Tip won't entertain it. He's fifteen now and he's been sleeping out there since he were a pup. I remember when me father was alive he tried all ways to get t'awd feller to sleep inside but it was no good.'

I looked at the old dog in amazement. I could see him more clearly now; he wasn't the typical sheepdog type, he was bigger-boned, longer in the hair, and he projected a bursting vitality that didn't go with his fifteen years. It was difficult to believe that any animal living in these bleak uplands should choose to sleep outside – and thrive on it. I had to look closely to see any sign of his great age. There was the slightest stiffness in his gait as he moved around, perhaps a fleshless look about his head and face and, of course, the tell-tale lens opacity in the depths of his eyes. But the general impression was of an unquenchable jauntiness.

He shook the last of the snow from his coat, pranced jerkily up to the farmer and gave a couple of reedy barks. Peter Trenholm laughed. 'You see he's ready to be off – he's a beggar for work is Tip.' He led the way towards the buildings and I followed, stumbling over the frozen ruts, like iron under the snow, and bending my head against the knife-like wind. It was a relief to open the byre door and escape into the sweet bovine warmth.

There was a fair mixture of animals in the long building. The dairy cows took up most of the length, then there were a few young heifers, some bullocks and finally, in an empty stall deeply bedded with straw, the other farm dogs. The cats were there too, so it had to be warm. No animal is a better judge of comfort than a cat and they were just visible as furry balls in the straw. They had the best place, up against the wooden partition where the warmth came through from the big animals.

Tip strode confidently among his colleagues – a young dog and a bitch with three half-grown pups. You could see he was boss.

One of the bullocks was my patient and he was looking a bit better. When I had seen him yesterday his rumen (the big first stomach) had been completely static and atonic following an over-eager consumption of frozen turnips. He had been slightly bloated and groaning with discomfort. But today as I leaned with my ear against his left side I could hear the beginnings of the surge and rumble of the normal rumen instead of the deathly silence of yesterday. My gastric lavage had undoubtedly tickled things up and I felt that another of the same would just about put him right. Almost lovingly I got together the ingredients of one of my favourite treatments, long since washed away in the flood of progress; the ounce of formalin, the half-pound of common salt, the can of black treacle from the barrel which you used to find in most cow houses, all mixed up in a bucket with two gallons of hot water.

I jammed the wooden gag into the bullock's mouth and buckled it behind the horns, then as Peter held the handles I passed the stomach tube down into the rumen and pumped in the mixture. When I had finished the bullock opened his eyes wide in surprise and began to paddle his hind legs. Listening again at his side, I could hear the reassuring bubbling of the stomach contents. I smiled to myself in satisfaction. It worked, it always worked.

Wiping down the tube I could hear the hiss-hiss as Peter's brother got on with the morning's milking, and as I prepared to leave he came down the byre with a full bucket on the way to the cooler. As he passed the dogs' stall he tipped a few pints of the warm milk into their dishes and Tip strolled forward casually for his breakfast. While he was drinking, the young dog tried to push his way in, but a soundless snap from Tip's jaws missed his nose by a fraction and he retired to another dish. I noticed, however, that the old dog made no protest as the bitch and pups joined him. The cats, black-and-white, tortoiseshell, tabby-grey, appeared, stretching, from the straw and advanced in a watchful ring. Their turn would come.

Mrs Trenholm called me in for a cup of tea and when I came out it was full daylight. But the sky was a burdened grey, and the sparse trees near the house strained their bare branches against the wind, which drove in long, icy gusts over the white empty miles of moor. It was what the Yorkshiremen called a 'thin wind' or sometimes a 'lazy wind' – the kind that couldn't be bothered to blow round you but went straight through instead. It made me feel that the best place on earth was by the side of that bright fire in the farmhouse kitchen.

Most people would have felt like that, but not old Tip. He

was capering around as Peter loaded a flat cart with some hay bales for the young cattle in the outside barns; then, as Peter started up the tractor, he leapt on to the back of the cart.

As I threw my tackle into the boot of the car I looked back at the old dog, legs braced against the uneven motion, tail waving, barking defiance at the cold world. I carried away the memory of Tip who scorned the softer things and slept in what he considered the place of honour – at his master's door.

A little incident like this has always been able to brighten my day and, fortunately, I have the kind of job where things of this kind happened. And sometimes it isn't even a happening – just a single luminous phrase.

As when I was examining a cow one morning while its neighbour was being milked. The milker was an old man and he was having trouble. He was sitting well into the cow, his cloth-capped head buried in her flank, the bucket gripped tightly between his knees, but the stool kept rocking about as the cow fidgeted and weaved. Twice she kicked the bucket over and she had an additional little trick of anointing her tail with particularly liquid faeces then lashing the old man across the face with it.

Finally he could stand it no longer. Leaping to his feet he dealt a puny blow at the cow's craggy back and emitted an exasperated shout.

'Stand still, thou shittin' awd bovril!'

•

Or the day when I had to visit Luke Benson at his smallholding in Hillom village. Luke was a powerful man of about sixty and had the unusual characteristic of speaking always through his clenched teeth. He literally articulated every word by moving only his lips, showing the rows of square, horse-like incisors clamped tightly together. It lent a peculiar intensity to his simplest utterance; and as he spoke, his eyes glared.

Most of his conversation consisted of scathing remarks about the other inhabitants of Hillom. In fact, he seemed to harbour a cordial dislike of the human race in general. Yet, strangely enough, I found him a very reasonable man to deal with; he accepted my diagnoses of his animals' ailments without question and appeared to be trying to be friendly by addressing me repeatedly as 'Jems', which was the nearest he could get to my name with his teeth together.

His fiercest hatred was reserved for his neighbour and fellow smallholder, a little lame man called Gill, to whom Luke referred invariably and unkindly as 'yon 'oppin youth'. A bitter feud had raged between them for many years, and I had seen Luke smile on only two occasions – once when Mr Gill's sow lost its litter and again when he had a stack burnt down.

When Mr Gill's wife ran away with a man who came round the farms selling brushes it caused a sensation. Nothing like that had ever happened in Hillom before, and a wave of delighted horror swept through the village. This, I thought, would be the high point of Luke Benson's life and when I had to visit a heifer of his I expected to find him jubilant. But Luke was gloomy.

As I examined and treated his animal he remained silent, and it wasn't until I went into the kitchen to wash my hands that he spoke. He glanced round warily at his wife, a gaunt, grim-faced woman who was applying blacklead to the grate.

'You'll have heard about yon 'oppin youth's missus runnin' off?' he said.

'Yes,' I replied. 'I did hear about it.' I waited for Luke to gloat but he seemed strangely ill at ease. He fidgeted until I had finished drying my hands, then he glared at me and bared his strong teeth.

'Ah'll tell you something, Jems,' he ground out. 'Ah wish somebody would tek MA bugger!'

And there was that letter from the Bramleys – that really made me feel good. You don't find people like the Bramleys now; radio, television and the motorcar have carried the outside world into the most isolated places, so that the simple people you used to meet on the lonely farms are rapidly becoming like people anywhere else. There are still a few left, of course – old folk who cling to the ways of their fathers – and when I come across any of them I like to make some excuse to sit down and talk with them and listen to the old Yorkshire words and expressions which have almost disappeared.

But even in the thirties, when there were many places still untouched by the flood of progress, the Bramleys were in some ways unique. There were four of them: three brothers, all middle-aged bachelors, and an older sister, also unmarried, and their farm lay in a wide, shallow depression in the hills. You could just see the ancient tiles of Scar House through the top branches of the sheltering trees if you stood outside the pub in Drewburn village, and in the summer it was possible to drive down over the fields to the farm. I had done it a few times, the bottles in the boot jingling and crashing as the car bounced over the rig and furrow. The other approach to the place was right on the other side through Mr Broom's stackyard and then along a track with ruts so deep that only a tractor could negotiate it.

There was, in fact, no road to the farm, but that didn't bother the Bramleys because the outside world held no great attraction for them. Miss Bramley made occasional trips to Darrowby on market days for provisions, and Herbert, the middle brother, had come into town in the spring of 1929 to have a tooth out, but apart from that they stayed contentedly at home.

A call to Scar House always came as rather a jolt because it meant that at least two hours had been removed from the working day. In all but the driest weather it was safer to leave the car at Mr Broom's and make the journey on foot. One February night at about eight o'clock I was splashing my way along the track, feeling the mud sucking at my wellingtons; it was to see a horse with colic, and my pockets were stuffed with everything I might need. My eyes were half closed against the steady drizzle, but some way ahead I could see the lights of the house winking among the trees.

After twenty minutes of slithering in and out of the unseen puddles and opening a series of broken, string-tied gates, I reached the farmyard and crossed over to the back door. I was about to knock when I stopped with my hand poised. I found I was looking through the kitchen window and in the interior, dimly lit by an oil lamp, the Bramleys were sitting in a row.

They weren't grouped round the fire but were jammed tightly on a long, high-backed wooden settle which stood against the far wall. The strange thing was the similarity of their attitudes; all four had their arms folded, chins resting on their chests, feet stretched out in front of them. The men had removed their heavy boots and were in their stockinged feet, but Miss Bramley wore an old pair of carpet slippers.

I stared, fascinated by the curious immobility of the group. They were not asleep, not talking or reading or listening to the radio – in fact, they didn't have one – they were just sitting.

I had never seen people just sitting before, and I stood there for some minutes to see if they would make a move or do anything at all, but nothing happened. It occurred to me that this was probably a typical evening; they worked hard all day, had their meal, then they just sat until bedtime.

A month or two later I discovered another unsuspected side of the Bramleys when they started having trouble with their cats. I knew they were fond of cats by the number and variety which swarmed over the place and perched confidently on my car bonnet on cold days with their unerring instinct for a warm place. But I was unprepared for the family's utter desolation when the cats started to die. Miss Bramley was on the doorstep at Skeldale House nearly every day carrying an egg basket with another pitiful patient – a cat or sometimes a few tiny kittens – huddling miserably inside.

Even today, with the full range of modern antibiotics, the treatment of feline enteritis is unrewarding and I had little success with my salicylates and non-specific injections. I did my best. I even took some of the cats in and kept them at the surgery so that I could attend them several times a day, but the mortality rate was high.

The Bramleys were stricken as they saw their cats diminishing. I was surprised at their grief because most farmers look on cats as pest killers and nothing more. But when Miss Bramley came in one morning with a fresh consignment of invalids she was in a sorry state. She stared at me across the surgery table, and her rough fingers clasped and unclasped on the handle of the egg basket.

'Is it going to go through 'em all?' she quavered.

'Well, it's very infectious and it looks as though most of your young cats will get it.'

For a moment Miss Bramley seemed to be struggling with herself, then her chin began to jerk and her whole face twitched uncontrollably. She didn't actually break down, but her eyes brimmed and a couple of tears wandered among the network of wrinkles on her cheeks. I looked at her helplessly as she stood there, wisps of grey hair straggling untidily from under the incongruous black beret which she wore pulled tightly over her ears.

'It's Topsy's kittens I'm worried about,' she gasped out at length. 'There's five of 'em, and they're the best we've got.'

I rubbed my chin. I had heard a lot about Topsy, one of a strain of incomparable ratters and mousers. Her last family were only about ten weeks old, and it would be a crushing blow to the Bramleys if anything happened to them. But what the devil could I do? There was, as yet, no protective vaccine against the disease – or, wait a minute, was there? I remembered that I'd heard a rumour that Burroughs Wellcome were working on one.

I pulled out a chair. 'Just sit down a few minutes, Miss Bramley. I'm going to make a phone call.' I was soon through to the Wellcome Laboratory and half expected a sarcastic reply. But they were kind and cooperative. They had had encouraging results with the new vaccine and would be glad to let me have five doses if I would inform them of the result.

I hurried back to Miss Bramley. 'I've ordered something for your kittens. I can't guarantee anything but there's nothing else to do. Have them down here on Tuesday morning.'

The vaccine arrived promptly, and as I injected the little creatures Miss Bramley extolled the virtues of the Topsy line. 'Look at the size of them ears! Did you ever see bigger 'uns on kittens?'

 I had to admit that I hadn't. The ears were enormous,

sail-like, and they made the ravishingly pretty little faces look even smaller.

Miss Bramley nodded and smiled with satisfaction. 'Aye, you can allus tell. It's the sure sign of a good mouser.'

The injection was repeated a week later. The kittens were still looking well.

'Well, that's it,' I said. 'We'll just have to wait now. But, remember, I want to know the outcome of this, so please don't forget to let me know.'

I didn't hear from the Bramleys for several months and had almost forgotten about the little experiment when I came upon a grubby envelope which had apparently been pushed under the surgery door. It was the promised report and was, in its way, a model of conciseness. It communicated all the information I required without frills or verbiage.

It was in a careful, spidery scrawl and said simply: 'Dere Sir, Them kittens is now big cats. Yrs trly, R. Bramley.'

Christmas Day

This was a different kind of ringing. I had gone to sleep as the great bells in the church tower down the street pealed for the Christmas midnight service, but this was a sharper, shriller sound.

It was difficult at first to shake off the mantle of unreality in which I had wrapped myself last night. Last night – Christmas Eve. It had been like a culmination of all the ideas I had ever held about Christmas – a flowering of emotions I had never experienced before. It had been growing in me since the afternoon call to a tiny village where the snow lay deep on the single street and on the walls and on the ledges of the windows where the lights on the tinselled trees glowed red and blue and gold; and as I left it in the dusk I drove beneath the laden branches of a group of dark spruce as motionless as though they had been sketched against the white background of the fields. And when I reached Darrowby it was dark, and around the market place the little shops were bright with decorations and the light from their windows fell in a soft yellow wash over the trodden snow of the cobbles. People, anonymously muffled, were hurrying about, doing their last-minute shopping, their feet slithering over the rounded stones.

I had known many Christmases in Scotland, but they had

taken second place to the New Year celebrations; there had been none of this air of subdued excitement which started days before, with folks shouting good wishes and coloured lights winking on the lonely fellsides and the farmers' wives plucking the fat geese, the feathers piled deep around their feet. And for fully two weeks you heard the children piping carols in the street, then knocking on the door for sixpences. And, best of all, last night the Methodist choir had sung out there, filling the night air with rich, thrilling harmony.

Before going to bed and just as the church bells began I closed the door of Skeldale House behind me and walked again into the market place. Nothing stirred now in the white square, stretching smooth and cold and empty under the moon, and there was a Dickensian look about the ring of houses and shops put together long before anybody thought of town planning; tall and short, fat and thin, squashed in crazily around the cobbles, their snow-burdened roofs jagged and uneven against the frosty sky.

As I walked back, the snow crunching under my feet, the bells clanging, the sharp air tingling in my nostrils, the wonder and mystery of Christmas enveloped me in a great wave. Peace on earth, goodwill towards men; the words became meaningful as never before and I saw myself suddenly as a tiny particle in the scheme of things: Darrowby, the farmers, the animals and me seemed for the first time like a warm, comfortable entity. I hadn't been drinking but I almost floated up the stairs to the bedroom.

Helen was still asleep, and as I crawled between the sheets

beside her I was still wallowing in my Yuletide euphoria. There wouldn't be much work tomorrow; we'd have a long lie-in – maybe until nine – and then a lazy day, a glorious hiatus in our busy life. As I drifted into sleep it was as though I was surrounded by the smiling faces of my clients looking down at me with an all-embracing benevolence; and strangely I fancied I could hear singing, sweet and haunting, just like the Methodist choir – 'God rest ye merry, gentlemen' . . .

But now there was this other bell which wouldn't stop. Must be the alarm. But as I pawed at the clock the noise continued and I saw that it was six o'clock. It was the telephone, of course. I lifted the receiver.

A metallic voice, crisp and very wide awake, jarred in my ear. 'Is that the vet?'

'Yes, Herriot speaking,' I mumbled.

'This is Brown, Willet Hill. I've got a cow down with milk fever. I want you here quick.'

'Right, I'll see to it.'

'Don't take ower long.' Then a click at the far end.

I rolled on to my back and stared at the ceiling. So this was Christmas Day. The day when I was going to step out of the world for a spell and luxuriate in the seasonal spirit. I hadn't bargained for this fellow jerking me brutally back to reality. And not a word of regret or apology. No 'Sorry to get you out of bed' or anything else, never mind 'Merry Christmas'. It was just a bit hard.

Mr Brown was waiting for me in the darkness of the

farmyard. I had been to his place a few times before, and as my headlights blazed on him I was struck, as always, by his appearance of perfect physical fitness. He was a gingery man of about forty with high cheekbones set in a sharp-featured, clear-skinned face. Red hair peeped from under a check cap, and a faint auburn down covered his cheeks, his neck, the backs of his hands. It made me feel a bit sleepier just to look at him.

He didn't say good morning but nodded briefly, then jerked his head in the direction of the byre. 'She's in there' was all he said.

He watched in silence as I gave the injections, and it wasn't until I was putting the empty bottles into my pocket that he spoke.

'Don't suppose I'll have to milk her today?'

'No,' I replied. 'Better leave the bag full.'

'Anything special about feedin'?'

'No, she can have anything she likes when she wants it.' Mr Brown was very efficient. Always wanted to know every detail.

As we crossed the yard he halted suddenly and turned to face me. Could it be that he was going to ask me in for a nice hot cup of tea?

'You know,' he said, as I stood ankle-deep in the snow, the frosty air nipping at my ears, 'I've had a few of these cases lately. Maybe there's summat wrong with my routine. Do you think I'm steaming up my cows too much?'

'It's quite possible.' I hurried towards the car. One thing I wasn't going to do was deliver a lecture on animal husbandry at this moment.

My hand was on the door handle when he said, 'I'll give you another ring if she's not up by dinner time. And there's one other thing – that was a hell of a bill I had from you fellers last month, so tell your boss not to be so savage with 'is pen.' Then he turned and walked quickly towards the house.

Well, that was nice, I thought as I drove away. Not even thanks or goodbye, just a complaint and a promise to haul me away from my roast goose if necessary. A sudden wave of anger surged in me. Bloody farmers! There were some miserable devils among them. Mr Brown had doused my festive feeling as effectively as if he had thrown a bucket of water over me.

As I mounted the steps of Skeldale House the darkness had paled to a shivery grey. Helen met me in the passage. She was carrying a tray.

'I'm sorry, Jim,' she said, 'but there's another urgent job. Siegfried's had to go out, too. But I've got a cup of coffee and some fried bread for you. Come in and sit down – you've got time to eat it before you go.'

I sighed. It was going to be just another day after all. 'What's this one about, Helen?' I asked, sipping the coffee.

'It's old Mr Kirby,' she replied. 'He's very worried about his nanny goat.'

'Nanny goat!'

'Yes, he says she's choking.'

'Choking! How the heck can she be choking?' I shouted.

'I really don't know. And I wish you wouldn't shout at me, Jim. It's not my fault.'

In an instant I was engulfed by shame. Here I was, in a bad temper, taking it out on my wife. It is a common reaction for vets to blame the hapless person who passes on an unwanted message, but I am not proud of it. I held out my hand and Helen took it.

'I'm sorry,' I said and finished the coffee sheepishly. My feeling of goodwill was at a very low ebb.

Mr Kirby was a retired farmer, but he had sensibly bought a cottage with a bit of land where he kept enough stock to occupy his time – a cow, a few pigs and his beloved goats. He had always had goats, even when he was running his dairy herd; he had a thing about them.

The cottage was in a village high up the dale. Mr Kirby met me at the gate.

'Ee, lad,' he said, 'I'm right sorry to be bothering you this early in the morning and Christmas an' all, but I didn't have no choice. Dorothy's real bad.'

He led the way to a stone shed which had been converted into a row of pens. Behind the wire of one of them a large white Saanen goat peered out at us anxiously, and as I watched her she gulped, gave a series of retching coughs, then stood trembling, saliva drooling from her mouth.

The farmer turned to me, wide-eyed. 'You see. I had to get you out, didn't I? If I left her till tomorrow she'd be a goner.'

'You're right, Mr Kirby,' I replied. 'You couldn't leave her. There's something in her throat.'

We went into the pen, and as the old man held the goat against the wall I tried to open her mouth. She didn't like it very much: as I prised her jaws apart, she startled me with a loud, long-drawn-out, human-sounding cry. It wasn't a big mouth but I have a small hand and, as the sharp back teeth tried to nibble me, I poked a finger deep into the pharynx.

There was something there all right. I could just touch it but I couldn't get hold of it. Then the animal began to throw her head about and I had to come out; I stood there, saliva dripping from my hand, looking thoughtfully at Dorothy.

After a few moments I turned to the farmer. 'You know, this is a bit baffling. I can feel something in the back of her throat, but it's soft – like cloth. I'd been expecting to find a bit of twig, or something sharp sticking in there – it's funny what a goat will pick up when she's pottering around outside. But if it's cloth, what the heck is holding it there? Why hasn't she swallowed it down?'

'Aye, it's a rum 'un, isn't it?' The old man ran a gentle hand along the animal's back. 'Do you think she'll get rid of it herself? Maybe it'll just slip down.'

'No, I don't. It's stuck fast. God knows how, but it is. And I've got to get it out soon because she's beginning to blow up. Look there.' I pointed to the goat's bulging left side, and as I did so, Dorothy began another paroxysm of coughs which seemed almost to tear her apart.

Mr Kirby looked at me with a mute appeal, but just at that

moment I didn't see what I could do. Then I opened the door of the pen. 'I'm going to get my torch from the car. Maybe I can see something to explain this.'

The old man held the torch as I once more pulled the goat's mouth open and again heard the curious child-like wailing. It was when the animal was in full cry that I noticed something under the tongue – a thin, dark band.

'I can see what's holding the thing now,' I cried. 'It's hooked round the tongue with string or something.' Carefully I pushed my forefinger under the band and began to pull.

It wasn't string. It began to stretch as I pulled carefully at it . . . like elastic. Then it stopped stretching and I felt a real resistance . . . whatever was in the throat was beginning to move. I kept up a gentle traction and very slowly the mysterious obstruction came sliding up over the back of the tongue and into the mouth, and when it came within reach I let go of the elastic, grabbed the sodden mass and hauled it forth. It seemed as if there was no end to it – a long snake of dripping material nearly two feet long – but at last I had it out on to the straw of the pen.

Mr Kirby seized it and held it up and as he unravelled the mass wonderingly he gave a sudden cry.

'God 'elp us, it's me summer drawers!'

'Your *what*?'

'Me summer drawers. Ah don't like them long johns when weather gets warmer and I allus change into these little short 'uns. Missus was havin' a clear-out afore the end of t'year and she didn't know whether to wash 'em or mek them into dusters. She washed them at t'finish and Dorothy must have got 'em off the line.' He held up the tattered shorts and regarded them ruefully. 'By gaw, they'd seen better days, but I reckon Dorothy's fettled them this time.'

Then his body began to shake silently, a few low giggles escaped from him and finally he gave a great shout of laughter. It was an infectious laugh, and I joined in as I watched him. He went on for quite a long time and when he had finished he was leaning weakly against the wire netting.

'Me poor awd drawers,' he gasped, then leaned over and patted the goat's head. 'But as long as you're all right, lass, I'm not worried.'

'Oh, she'll be OK.' I pointed to her left flank. 'You can see her stomach's going down already.' As I spoke, Dorothy belched pleasurably and began to nose interestedly at her hay rack.

The farmer gazed at her fondly. 'Isn't that grand to see! She's ready for her grub again. And if she hadn't got her tongue round the elastic that lot would have gone right down and killed her.'

'I really don't think it would, you know,' I said. 'It's amazing what ruminants can carry around in their stomachs. I once found a bicycle tyre inside a cow when I was operating for something else. The tyre didn't seem to be bothering her in the least.'

'I see.' Mr Kirby rubbed his chin. 'So Dorothy might have wandered around with me drawers inside her for years.'

'It's possible. You'd never have known what became of them.'

'By gaw, that's right,' Mr Kirby said, and for a moment I thought he was going to start laughing again, but he mastered himself and seized my arm. 'But I don't know what I'm keeping you out here for, lad. You must come in and have a bit o' Christmas cake.'

Inside the tiny living-room of the cottage I was ushered to the best chair by the fireside where two rough logs blazed and crackled.

'Bring cake out for Mr Herriot, mother,' the farmer cried as he rummaged in the pantry. He reappeared with a bottle of whisky at the same time as his wife bustled in carrying a cake thickly laid with icing and ornamented with coloured spangles, toboggans, reindeer.

Mr Kirby unscrewed the stopper. 'You know, mother, we're lucky to have such men as this to come out on a Christmas mornin' to help us.'

'Aye, we are that.' The old lady cut a thick slice of the cake and placed it on a plate by the side of an enormous wedge of Wensleydale cheese.

Her husband meanwhile was pouring my drink. Yorkshiremen are amateurs with whisky and there was something delightfully untutored in the way he was sloshing it into the glass as if it were lemonade; he would have filled it to the brim if I hadn't stopped him.

Drink in hand, cake on knee, I looked across at the farmer and his wife, who were sitting in upright kitchen chairs watching me with quiet benevolence. The two faces had something in common – a kind of beauty. You would find faces like that only in the country; deeply wrinkled and weathered, clear-eyed, alight with a cheerful serenity.

I raised my glass. 'A happy Christmas to you both.'

The old couple nodded and replied smilingly. 'And the same to you, Mr Herriot.'

'Aye, and thanks again, lad,' said Mr Kirby. 'We're right grateful to you for runnin' out here to save awd Dorothy. We've maybe mucked up your day for you, but it would've mucked up ours if we'd lost the old lass, wouldn't it, mother?'

'Don't worry, you haven't spoiled anything for me,' I said. 'In fact, you've made me realize again that it really is Christmas.' And as I looked around the little room with the decorations hanging from the low-beamed ceiling I could feel the emotions of last night surging slowly back, a warmth creeping through me that had nothing to do with the whisky.

I took a bite of the cake and followed it with a moist slice of cheese. When I had first come to Yorkshire I had been aghast when offered this unheard-of combination, but time had brought wisdom and I had discovered that the mixture when chewed boldly together was exquisite; and, strangely, I had also found that there was nothing more suitable for washing it finally over the tonsils than a draught of raw whisky.

'You don't mind t'wireless, Mr Herriot?' Mrs Kirby asked.

'We always like to have it on Christmas morning to hear t'old hymns but I'll turn it off if you like.'

'No, please leave it, it sounds grand.' I turned to look at the old radio with its chipped wooden veneer, the ornate scroll-work over the worn fabric; it must have been one of the earliest models, and it gave off a tinny sound, but the singing of the church choir was none the less sweet, 'Hark the herald angels sing' flooding the little room, mingling with the splutter of the logs and the soft voices of the old people.

They showed me a picture of their son, who was a policeman over in Houlton, and their daughter, who was married to a neighbouring farmer. They were bringing their grandchildren up for Christmas dinner as they always did, and Mrs Kirby opened a box and ran a hand over the long row of crackers. The choir started on 'Once in royal David's city'. I finished my whisky and put up only feeble resistance as the farmer plied the bottle again. Through the small window I could see the bright berries of a holly tree pushing through their covering of snow.

It was really a shame to have to leave here and it was sadly that I drained my glass for the second time and scooped up the last crumbs of cake and icing from my plate.

Mr Kirby came out with me and at the gate of the cottage he stopped and held out his hand.

'Thank ye, lad, I'm right grateful,' he said. 'And all the very best to you.'

For a moment the rough, dry palm rasped against mine, then I was in the car, starting the engine. I looked at my watch; it was still only half past nine but the first early sunshine was sparkling from a sky of palest blue.

Beyond the village the road climbed steeply, then curved around the rim of the valley in a wide arc, and it was here that you came suddenly upon the whole great expanse of the Plain of York spread out almost at your feet. I always slowed down here and there was always something different to see, but today the vast chequerboard of fields and farms and woods stood out with a clarity I had never seen before. Maybe it was because this was a holiday and down there no factory chimney smoked, no lorries belched fumes, but the distance was magically foreshortened in the clear, frosty air, and I felt I could reach out and touch the familiar landmarks far below.

I looked back at the enormous white billows and folds of the fells, crowding close one upon another into the blue distance, every crevice uncannily defined, the highest summits glittering where the sun touched them. I could see the village with the Kirbys' cottage at the end. I had found Christmas and peace and goodwill and everything back there.

Farmers? They were the salt of the earth.

PENGUIN 60s

MARTIN AMIS · *God's Dice*
HANS CHRISTIAN ANDERSEN · *The Emperor's New Clothes*
MARCUS AURELIUS · *Meditations*
JAMES BALDWIN · *Sonny's Blues*
AMBROSE BIERCE · *An Occurrence at Owl Creek Bridge*
DIRK BOGARDE · *From Le Pigeonnier*
WILLIAM BOYD · *Killing Lizards*
POPPY Z. BRITE · *His Mouth will Taste of Wormwood*
ITALO CALVINO · *Ten Italian Folktales*
ALBERT CAMUS · *Summer*
TRUMAN CAPOTE · *First and Last*
RAYMOND CHANDLER · *Goldfish*
ANTON CHEKHOV · *The Black Monk*
ROALD DAHL · *Lamb to the Slaughter*
ELIZABETH DAVID · *I'll be with You in the Squeezing of a Lemon*
N. J. DAWOOD (TRANS.) · *The Seven Voyages of Sindbad the Sailor*
ISAK DINESEN · *The Dreaming Child*
SIR ARTHUR CONAN DOYLE · *The Man with the Twisted Lip*
DICK FRANCIS · *Racing Classics*
SIGMUND FREUD · *Five Lectures on Psycho-Analysis*
KAHLIL GIBRAN · *Prophet, Madman, Wanderer*
STEPHEN JAY GOULD · *Adam's Navel*
ALASDAIR GRAY · *Five Letters from an Eastern Empire*
GRAHAM GREENE · *Under the Garden*
JAMES HERRIOT · *Seven Yorkshire Tales*
PATRICIA HIGHSMITH · *Little Tales of Misogyny*
M. R. JAMES AND R. L. STEVENSON · *The Haunted Dolls' House*
RUDYARD KIPLING · *Baa Baa, Black Sheep*
PENELOPE LIVELY · *A Long Night at Abu Simbel*
KATHERINE MANSFIELD · *The Escape*

PENGUIN 60s

GABRIEL GARCÍA MÁRQUEZ · *Bon Voyage, Mr President*
PATRICK MCGRATH · *The Angel*
HERMAN MELVILLE · *Bartleby*
SPIKE MILLIGAN · *Gunner Milligan, 954024*
MICHEL DE MONTAIGNE · *Four Essays*
JAN MORRIS · *From the Four Corners*
JOHN MORTIMER · *Rumpole and the Younger Generation*
R. K. NARAYAN · *Tales from Malgudi*
ANAÏS NIN · *A Model*
FRANK O'CONNOR · *The Genius*
GEORGE ORWELL · *Pages from a Scullion's Diary*
CAMILLE PAGLIA · *Sex and Violence, or Nature and Art*
SARA PARETSKY · *A Taste of Life*
EDGAR ALLAN POE · *The Pit and the Pendulum*
MISS READ · *Village Christmas*
JEAN RHYS · *Let Them Call It Jazz*
DAMON RUNYON · *The Snatching of Bookie Bob*
SAKI · *The Secret Sin of Septimus Brope*
WILL SELF · *Scale*
GEORGES SIMENON · *Death of a Nobody*
MURIEL SPARK · *The Portobello Road*
ROBERT LOUIS STEVENSON · *The Pavilion on the Links*
PAUL THEROUX · *Down the Yangtze*
WILLIAM TREVOR · *Matilda's England*
MARK TULLY · *Ram Chander's Story*
JOHN UPDIKE · *Friends from Philadelphia*
EUDORA WELTY · *Why I Live at the P. O.*
EDITH WHARTON · *Madame de Treymes*
OSCAR WILDE · *The Happy Prince*
VIRGINIA WOOLF · *Killing the Angel in the House*

READ MORE IN PENGUIN